Recorder Trios
from the Beginning

John Pitts

Ensemble playing brings pleasure to all involved, and with it an incentive to learn new notes and rhythms in order to succeed. Incidental development of listening skills and concentration is also required for success.

This collection of 14 mixed recorder trios is suitable for either three players or group ensembles. It features a wide range of repertoire which includes classical favourites, folk songs, spirituals, blues, a Christmas medley and Latin American and Caribbean items, together with original pieces by John Pitts.

The Teacher's Book contains easy piano accompaniments and chord symbols. The trios feature three different recorder groupings, with the music grouped into corresponding sections:

2 descants and treble
descant and 2 trebles
descant, treble and tenor

Within each section the music is graded so far as possible, both in range of notes (pitches) included and level of difficulty.

In each piece the musical interest is generally divided between all three instruments, so that all players have the opportunity to play the main tune.

In keeping with the 'repertoire' nature of the book, only a minimum of help or explanation is given. Where more help is required it is best to refer to the appropriate pages of the teaching scheme *Recorder from the Beginning*.

Chester Music Limited
(A division of Music Sales Limited)
8/9 Frith Street, London W1V 5TZ

895

Music processed by Stave Origination.
Cover photography by Patrick Harrison.
Cover design by Jon Forss.
Printed in the United Kingdom by Caligraving Limited, Thetford, Norfolk.

Contents

Little David Play On Your Harp   Spiritual

La Donna E Mobile (from Rigoletto) Verdi

Rondo (K.213) Mozart

11

Beckett Blues   Pitts

Go Down, Moses   Spiritual

Not too fast, with a swing

Christmas Spirituals

De Virgin Mary Had A Baby Boy

Rise Up Shepherd

22

The Gospel Train   Spiritual

St Anthony Chorale   Brahms

from Variations On A Theme Of Haydn

An Eriskay Love Lilt   Hebridean folk song

Yellow Bird Calypso

Las Heras Beguine   Pitts

American Patrol   F.W. Meacham

Calypso Carnival

Sloop John 'B'

48

Scott Joplin In Concert

Peacherine Rag

Recorder Duets *from the* Beginning

by John Pitts

**Three collections of easy duets
for descant recorders, complementing
the author's popular teaching scheme
Recorder from the Beginning.**

**These superb arrangements, ranging
from Beethoven to the Blues, bring all the
benefits and enjoyment of ensemble playing
and are suitable for 2 players or class
ensembles.**

**Precisely graded by level of difficulty of
notes included.**

**Guitar chords are included, along with
piano accompaniments and suggestions
for additional percussion accompaniments.**

Book 1 CH61213
Book 2 CH61214
Book 3 CH61215
Teacher's Book 1 CH61251
Teacher's Book 2 CH61252
Teacher's Book 3 CH61253

Descant & Treble Recorder Duets from the Beginning

**At last, a great collection of duets for treble
and descant! The interest is divided equally
between the two parts, and both are precisely
graded by level of difficulty and notes included.**

Pupil's Book CH61297
Teacher's Book CH61304

Chester Music Limited
(A division of Music Sales Limited)
8/9 Frith Street, London W1V 5TZ